Heavenly Hosts (V.) HELL UTD

Garry Kilworth   Mark Oliver

mammoth

For Christian and Conrad
G. K.

For Joe (Demons) and Sam (Angels)
M. O.

First published in Great Britain in 1998 by Mammoth
an imprint of Reed International Books Limited
Michelin House, 81 Fulham Road, London SW3 6RB

Text copyright © 1998 Garry Kilworth
Illustrations copyright © 1998 Mark Oliver

Epix is a Trade Mark of Reed International Books Limited

The rights of Garry Kilworth and Mark Oliver to be identified
as the author and illustrator of this work have
been asserted by them in accordance with the
Copyright, Designs and Patents Act 1988

ISBN   0 7497 3328 8

10 9 8 7 6 5 4 3 2 1

Mark Oliver is represented by ILLUSTRATION Ltd
London 0171 228 8882

A CIP catalogue record for this book is
available from the British Library

Printed by Selwood Printing Ltd
Burgess Hill, West Sussex, Great Britain

1

Your commentator Nostra Damus here, folks. How about this crazy weather?
Every match in the country has been rained off – bar one – a game between two schools. So we're going over there to cover the end of this battle of the giants . . . smallish giants . . .

Well, kids actually. But we're hoping for some **greeeaat football!**

Two players to look out for are David Keller, playing for Bridgenorth High Town and Peter Pickering, who's already scored a cracking goal for Bridgenorth Low Town. Both players are looking to impress the talent scout for the county team.

And not only the scout – there's Susan Danling, the best looking girl in Bridgenorth!

The ball drops at David's fe

He weaves through the opposition.

And a *stunning* shot puts the ball away.

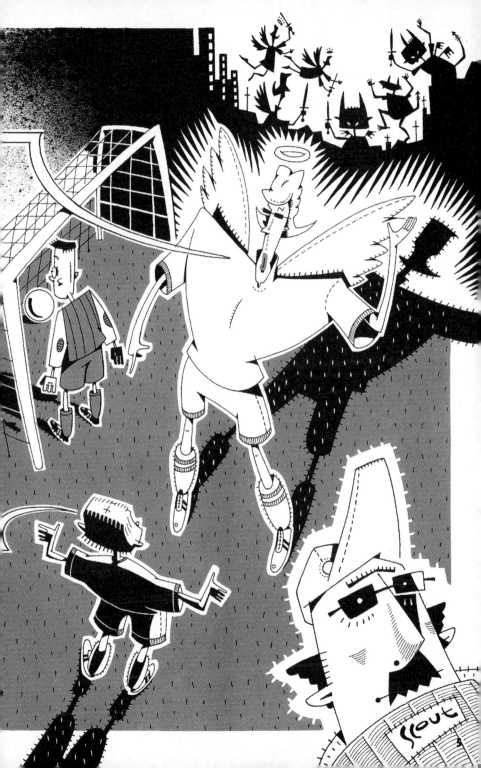

We're playing away today, so we have to go *down*.

6

Hi, folks, it's me again, Nostra 'The Prophet' Damus, here at the Armageddon Cup.

My forecast? I predict a win for one side and a defeat for the other ...**Wait,** here come the Angels, spruce and dapper as usual, followed by the Demons, predictably dirty and dishevelled – ha, ha!

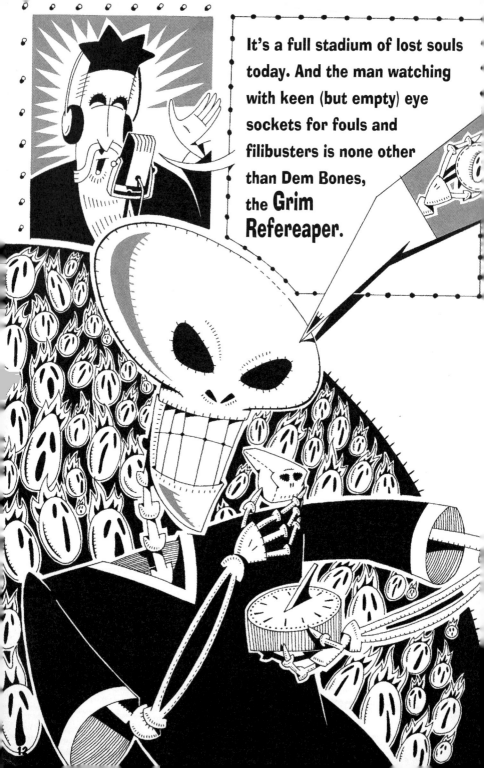

It's a full stadium of lost souls today. And the man watching with keen (but empty) eye sockets for fouls and filibusters is none other than **Dem Bones**, the **Grim Refereaper.**

15

Hell United have opened the scoring with a Beelzebub Bender, and they're celebrating with their famous Old Nick Shuffle. I'm afraid Heavenly Hosts deserved that.

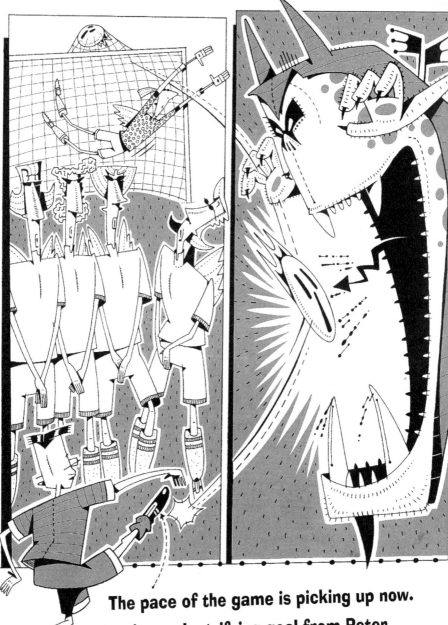

The pace of the game is picking up now.
Here's an electrifying goal from Peter
Pickering. No wonder he was brought in!

It's 2 – 1 to Hell United.

And look at the skill in this goal from David Keller to even the score. These two young strikers are devilishly divine!

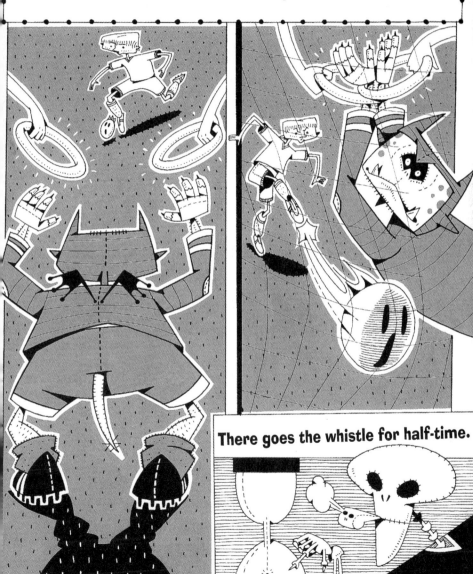

There goes the whistle for half-time.

The sands are halfway through the hour-glass, folks. Time to raid your fridges.

How about that goal, Pickering? It was a blinder.

That county scout would have snapped me up if he'd seen my last goal. We're going to win this match, Keller!

A
NG
ELS
ARE T
HE WIN
NERS

Soul-boy

You need faith — and lots of it! Tell yourselves: 'We are the Holy Joes! We are the immaculate! We are the most high!' Them? They've fallen from grace. They're lost. They're the pits.

Fire and brimstone, you sulphur-breathing beauties should be wiping the floor with those luvvies. You are the bogey-men and proud of it. Tread on their twinkle toes! Stomp on their pretty wings! Use their haloes for Frisbees!

Ankle Biters

And the second half has started with a **bang**, not a whimper. **Things are getting volcanic out there.**

29

The Demons are getting desperate . . .

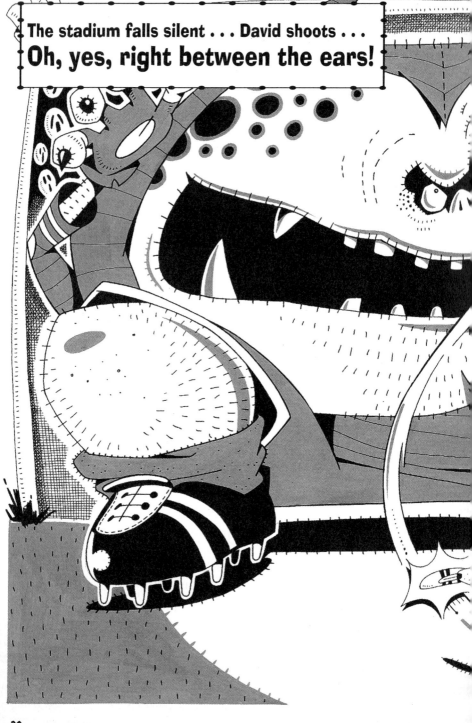

This exciting annual event is brought to a close with a fantastic penalty goal by David Keller. 350 matches have been played in the Armageddon Cup, and Heavenly Hosts are now one match ahead of Hell United. Don't forget to tune into this channel for next year's game.

Yes, yes! The Cup is ours for another year. Yehaaa!

Celebrations tonight! Bring out the tea and buttered crumpets!

All shook up, the Demons slink back to the locker rooms, followed by a jubilant team of Angels.

How the mighty have fallen! We were swifter than eagles. We were stronger than lions. Make way for David, king of footballers.

Back to Bridgenorth where the battle is yet to be fought and won.

Wow! Peter's as mad as fire now. Look at that goal within *five seconds.*

Nice game, lad. Listen, how would you like a chance to play for the county?

The county? You bet!

Peter, there's that wing-back who fed you the ball. Hasn't he got nice hair? Who is he? I think he's pretty nifty, don't you? I suspect he's probably your best player, isn't he? Is he going to be at the practice next week? I might come and watch, you know, just for something to do . . .

And I hope the Angels ask me! It was really cool, Peter. Well, one place was – the other was a bit hot. Listen, how about some header practice, Saturday . . .?